# 25 Days of Bible Verses for Mothers

## A Christian Devotional & Coloring Journal

written & designed by Shalana Frisby

Get organized for success in your Bible study!
Download your bonus free printables now:

# WWW.123JOURNALIT.COM / FREEBIES
SCRIPTURE FLASHCARDS - BIBLE READING PROMPTS - JOURNALING PAGES

More information at: www.123journalit.com

First Printing: October 2018
1 2 3 Journal It Publishing

ISBN-13: 978-1-947209-91-6
*25 Days of Bible Verses Series: Mothers Edition*

This journal belongs to

_____

_____

_____

# How to use this journal:

Find a quiet place and start with prayer asking for guidance.

Write the included daily verses using your preferred bible version.

Dig deeper by filling in the sections on the study notes page.

Journal reflections about life and your additional notes.

Get creative by coloring, doodling, and drawing.

...have fun hiding God's Word in your heart...

# Write, Reflect, & Repeat Daily

PRAY & WRITE TODAY'S VERSE:
Psalm 139:13-14

STUDY NOTES: what does this scripture mean?

TODAY'S date: _____

PRAYER REQUESTS
for my family & children

DIG DEEPER: how does it apply to my life?

GIVE THANKS
what I'm grateful for today

REFLECTIONS & NOTES:

# The 25 Bible Verses Featured:

Psalm 139:13-14

Nahum 1:3

Ecclesiastes 3:1-8

1 Corinthians 12:12-14

James 3:1-5

Isaiah 49:13-16

Deuteronomy 4:39-40

Matthew 12:33-37

1 Peter 4:12-14

Genesis 3:1-7

Luke 3:7-14

Acts 12:9-11

James 4:11-12

Deuteronomy 6:6-7

Joshua 1:5

Exodus 14:14

Jude 1:20-23

Galatians 5:22-26

Galatians 5:14-15

Philippians 4:12-13

Ruth 1:16-18

Ephesians 5:8-11

Proverbs 31:25-31

Psalm 127:3-5

John 3:16-18

PRAY & WRITE TODAY'S VERSE:
*Psalm 139:13-14*

## STUDY NOTES: *what does this scripture mean?*

_____
_____
_____
_____
_____
_____
_____
_____
_____

## TODAY'S *date:* _____

### PRAYER REQUESTS
*for my family & children:*

. . . . . . . . . . . . . . . . . . . . . . . . . . . . . . . . . .
. . . . . . . . . . . . . . . . . . . . . . . . . . . . . . . . . .
. . . . . . . . . . . . . . . . . . . . . . . . . . . . . . . . . .
. . . . . . . . . . . . . . . . . . . . . . . . . . . . . . . . . .
. . . . . . . . . . . . . . . . . . . . . . . . . . . . . . . . . .
. . . . . . . . . . . . . . . . . . . . . . . . . . . . . . . . . .
. . . . . . . . . . . . . . . . . . . . . . . . . . . . . . . . . .

## DIG DEEPER: *how does it apply to my life?*

_____
_____
_____
_____
_____
_____
_____
_____

### GIVE THANKS
*what I'm grateful for today:*

. . . . . . . . . . . . . . . . . . . . . . . . . . . . . . . . . .
. . . . . . . . . . . . . . . . . . . . . . . . . . . . . . . . . .
. . . . . . . . . . . . . . . . . . . . . . . . . . . . . . . . . .
. . . . . . . . . . . . . . . . . . . . . . . . . . . . . . . . . .
. . . . . . . . . . . . . . . . . . . . . . . . . . . . . . . . . .
. . . . . . . . . . . . . . . . . . . . . . . . . . . . . . . . . .
. . . . . . . . . . . . . . . . . . . . . . . . . . . . . . . . . .

# REFLECTIONS & NOTES:

_____

_____

_____

_____

_____

_____

_____

_____

_____

_____

_____

_____

_____

_____

_____

_____

_____

_____

PRAY & WRITE TODAY'S VERSE:
Nahum 1:3

## STUDY NOTES: what does this scripture mean?

_____
_____
_____
_____
_____
_____
_____
_____
_____

## DIG DEEPER: how does it apply to my life?

_____
_____
_____
_____
_____
_____
_____
_____

## TODAY'S date: _____

### PRAYER REQUESTS
for my family & children:

· · · · · · · · · · · · · · · · · · · · · · · · · ·
· · · · · · · · · · · · · · · · · · · · · · · · · ·
· · · · · · · · · · · · · · · · · · · · · · · · · ·
· · · · · · · · · · · · · · · · · · · · · · · · · ·
· · · · · · · · · · · · · · · · · · · · · · · · · ·
· · · · · · · · · · · · · · · · · · · · · · · · · ·
· · · · · · · · · · · · · · · · · · · · · · · · · ·
· · · · · · · · · · · · · · · · · · · · · · · · · ·

### GIVE THANKS
what I'm grateful for today:

· · · · · · · · · · · · · · · · · · · · · · · · · ·
· · · · · · · · · · · · · · · · · · · · · · · · · ·
· · · · · · · · · · · · · · · · · · · · · · · · · ·
· · · · · · · · · · · · · · · · · · · · · · · · · ·
· · · · · · · · · · · · · · · · · · · · · · · · · ·
· · · · · · · · · · · · · · · · · · · · · · · · · ·
· · · · · · · · · · · · · · · · · · · · · · · · · ·
· · · · · · · · · · · · · · · · · · · · · · · · · ·

# REFLECTIONS & NOTES:

PRAY & WRITE TODAY'S VERSE:
*Ecclesiastes 3:1—8*

## STUDY NOTES: what does this scripture mean?

_____
_____
_____
_____
_____
_____
_____
_____
_____
_____

## DIG DEEPER: how does it apply to my life?

_____
_____
_____
_____
_____
_____
_____
_____

## TODAY'S date: _____

### PRAYER REQUESTS
for my family & children:

. . . . . . . . . . . . . . . . . . . . . . . . .
. . . . . . . . . . . . . . . . . . . . . . . . .
. . . . . . . . . . . . . . . . . . . . . . . . .
. . . . . . . . . . . . . . . . . . . . . . . . .
. . . . . . . . . . . . . . . . . . . . . . . . .
. . . . . . . . . . . . . . . . . . . . . . . . .
. . . . . . . . . . . . . . . . . . . . . . . . .
. . . . . . . . . . . . . . . . . . . . . . . . .

### GIVE THANKS
what I'm grateful for today:

. . . . . . . . . . . . . . . . . . . . . . . . .
. . . . . . . . . . . . . . . . . . . . . . . . .
. . . . . . . . . . . . . . . . . . . . . . . . .
. . . . . . . . . . . . . . . . . . . . . . . . .
. . . . . . . . . . . . . . . . . . . . . . . . .
. . . . . . . . . . . . . . . . . . . . . . . . .
. . . . . . . . . . . . . . . . . . . . . . . . .

# REFLECTIONS & NOTES:

_____

_____

_____

_____

_____

_____

_____

_____

_____

_____

_____

_____

_____

_____

_____

_____

_____

PRAY & WRITE TODAY'S VERSE:
1 Corinthians 12:12-14

# STUDY NOTES: what does this scripture mean?

_____
_____
_____
_____
_____
_____
_____
_____
_____
_____

# DIG DEEPER: how does it apply to my life?

_____
_____
_____
_____
_____
_____
_____
_____
_____

## TODAY'S date: _____

### PRAYER REQUESTS
for my family & children:

.................................
.................................
.................................
.................................
.................................
.................................
.................................
.................................

### GIVE THANKS
what I'm grateful for today:

.................................
.................................
.................................
.................................
.................................
.................................
.................................
.................................

23

# REFLECTIONS & NOTES:

PRAY & WRITE TODAY'S VERSE:
James 3:1-5

_____
_____
_____
_____
_____
_____
_____
_____
_____
_____
_____
_____
_____

## STUDY NOTES: what does this scripture mean?

_____
_____
_____
_____
_____
_____
_____
_____
_____
_____

## DIG DEEPER: how does it apply to my life?

_____
_____
_____
_____
_____
_____
_____
_____
_____

TODAY'S date: _____

## PRAYER REQUESTS
for my family & children:

.....................................
.....................................
.....................................
.....................................
.....................................
.....................................
.....................................
.....................................
.....................................

## GIVE THANKS
what I'm grateful for today:

.....................................
.....................................
.....................................
.....................................
.....................................
.....................................
.....................................
.....................................

# REFLECTIONS & NOTES:

PRAY & WRITE TODAY'S VERSE:
Isaiah 49:13-16

# STUDY NOTES: what does this scripture mean?

_____
_____
_____
_____
_____
_____
_____
_____
_____
_____

# DIG DEEPER: how does it apply to my life?

_____
_____
_____
_____
_____
_____
_____
_____
_____

TODAY'S date: _____

## PRAYER REQUESTS
for my family & children:

.............................................
.............................................
.............................................
.............................................
.............................................
.............................................
.............................................
.............................................

## GIVE THANKS
what I'm grateful for today:

.............................................
.............................................
.............................................
.............................................
.............................................
.............................................
.............................................
.............................................

# REFLECTIONS & NOTES:

PRAY & WRITE TODAY'S VERSE:
Deuteronomy 4:39-40

# STUDY NOTES: what does this scripture mean?

_____
_____
_____
_____
_____
_____
_____
_____
_____
_____

# DIG DEEPER: how does it apply to my life?

_____
_____
_____
_____
_____
_____
_____
_____
_____

TODAY'S date: _____

## PRAYER REQUESTS
### for my family & children:

. . . . . . . . . . . . . . . . . . . . . . . . . . . .
. . . . . . . . . . . . . . . . . . . . . . . . . . . .
. . . . . . . . . . . . . . . . . . . . . . . . . . . .
. . . . . . . . . . . . . . . . . . . . . . . . . . . .
. . . . . . . . . . . . . . . . . . . . . . . . . . . .
. . . . . . . . . . . . . . . . . . . . . . . . . . . .
. . . . . . . . . . . . . . . . . . . . . . . . . . . .
. . . . . . . . . . . . . . . . . . . . . . . . . . . .
. . . . . . . . . . . . . . . . . . . . . . . . . . . .

## GIVE THANKS
### what I'm grateful for today:

. . . . . . . . . . . . . . . . . . . . . . . . . . . .
. . . . . . . . . . . . . . . . . . . . . . . . . . . .
. . . . . . . . . . . . . . . . . . . . . . . . . . . .
. . . . . . . . . . . . . . . . . . . . . . . . . . . .
. . . . . . . . . . . . . . . . . . . . . . . . . . . .
. . . . . . . . . . . . . . . . . . . . . . . . . . . .
. . . . . . . . . . . . . . . . . . . . . . . . . . . .
. . . . . . . . . . . . . . . . . . . . . . . . . . . .
. . . . . . . . . . . . . . . . . . . . . . . . . . . .

# REFLECTIONS & NOTES:

PRAY & WRITE TODAY'S VERSE:
Matthew 12:33-37

## STUDY NOTES: what does this scripture mean?

_____
_____
_____
_____
_____
_____
_____
_____
_____
_____

## DIG DEEPER: how does it apply to my life?

_____
_____
_____
_____
_____
_____
_____
_____

TODAY'S date: _____

### PRAYER REQUESTS
for my family & children:

............................................
............................................
............................................
............................................
............................................
............................................
............................................
............................................

### GIVE THANKS
what I'm grateful for today:

............................................
............................................
............................................
............................................
............................................
............................................
............................................
............................................

39

# REFLECTIONS & NOTES:

## STUDY NOTES: what does this scripture mean?

TODAY'S date: _____

_____
_____
_____
_____
_____
_____
_____
_____
_____

### PRAYER REQUESTS
for my family & children:

. . . . . . . . . . . . . . . . . . . . . . . . . . .
. . . . . . . . . . . . . . . . . . . . . . . . . . .
. . . . . . . . . . . . . . . . . . . . . . . . . . .
. . . . . . . . . . . . . . . . . . . . . . . . . . .
. . . . . . . . . . . . . . . . . . . . . . . . . . .
. . . . . . . . . . . . . . . . . . . . . . . . . . .
. . . . . . . . . . . . . . . . . . . . . . . . . . .
. . . . . . . . . . . . . . . . . . . . . . . . . . .

## DIG DEEPER: how does it apply to my life?

_____
_____
_____
_____
_____
_____
_____
_____

### GIVE THANKS
what I'm grateful for today:

. . . . . . . . . . . . . . . . . . . . . . . . . . .
. . . . . . . . . . . . . . . . . . . . . . . . . . .
. . . . . . . . . . . . . . . . . . . . . . . . . . .
. . . . . . . . . . . . . . . . . . . . . . . . . . .
. . . . . . . . . . . . . . . . . . . . . . . . . . .
. . . . . . . . . . . . . . . . . . . . . . . . . . .
. . . . . . . . . . . . . . . . . . . . . . . . . . .

# REFLECTIONS & NOTES:

PRAY & WRITE TODAY'S VERSE:
Genesis 3:1-7

# STUDY NOTES: what does this scripture mean?

_____
_____
_____
_____
_____
_____
_____
_____
_____
_____

# DIG DEEPER: how does it apply to my life?

_____
_____
_____
_____
_____
_____
_____
_____

TODAY'S date: _____

## PRAYER REQUESTS
### for my family & children:

............................................
............................................
............................................
............................................
............................................
............................................
............................................
............................................
............................................

## GIVE THANKS
### what I'm grateful for today:

............................................
............................................
............................................
............................................
............................................
............................................
............................................
............................................
............................................

# REFLECTIONS & NOTES:

PRAY & WRITE TODAY'S VERSE:
Luke 3:7-14

# STUDY NOTES: what does this scripture mean?

_____
_____
_____
_____
_____
_____
_____
_____
_____
_____
_____

# TODAY'S date: _____

## PRAYER REQUESTS
### for my family & children:

........................................
........................................
........................................
........................................
........................................
........................................
........................................
........................................
........................................
........................................

# DIG DEEPER: how does it apply to my life?

_____
_____
_____
_____
_____
_____
_____
_____
_____

## GIVE THANKS
### what I'm grateful for today:

........................................
........................................
........................................
........................................
........................................
........................................
........................................
........................................

# REFLECTIONS & NOTES:

PRAY & WRITE TODAY'S VERSE:
Acts 12:9—11

## STUDY NOTES: *what does this scripture mean?*

_____
_____
_____
_____
_____
_____
_____
_____
_____

## DIG DEEPER: *how does it apply to my life?*

_____
_____
_____
_____
_____
_____
_____
_____

TODAY'S *date:* _____

## PRAYER REQUESTS
*for my family & children:*

........................................
........................................
........................................
........................................
........................................
........................................
........................................
........................................
........................................

## GIVE THANKS
*what I'm grateful for today:*

........................................
........................................
........................................
........................................
........................................
........................................
........................................
........................................

# REFLECTIONS & NOTES:

PRAY & WRITE TODAY'S VERSE:
James 4:11–12

_____
_____
_____
_____
_____
_____
_____
_____
_____
_____
_____
_____
_____

# STUDY NOTES: what does this scripture mean?

_____
_____
_____
_____
_____
_____
_____
_____
_____
_____

# DIG DEEPER: how does it apply to my life?

_____
_____
_____
_____
_____
_____
_____
_____
_____

TODAY'S date: _____

## PRAYER REQUESTS
### for my family & children:

.................................
.................................
.................................
.................................
.................................
.................................
.................................
.................................

## GIVE THANKS
### what I'm grateful for today:

.................................
.................................
.................................
.................................
.................................
.................................
.................................
.................................

# REFLECTIONS & NOTES:

PRAY & WRITE TODAY'S VERSE:
Deuteronomy 6:6-7

# STUDY NOTES: what does this scripture mean?

_____
_____
_____
_____
_____
_____
_____
_____
_____
_____

# DIG DEEPER: how does it apply to my life?

_____
_____
_____
_____
_____
_____
_____
_____

TODAY'S date: _____

## PRAYER REQUESTS
### for my family & children:

· · · · · · · · · · · · · · · · · · · · · · · · · · ·
· · · · · · · · · · · · · · · · · · · · · · · · · · ·
· · · · · · · · · · · · · · · · · · · · · · · · · · ·
· · · · · · · · · · · · · · · · · · · · · · · · · · ·
· · · · · · · · · · · · · · · · · · · · · · · · · · ·
· · · · · · · · · · · · · · · · · · · · · · · · · · ·
· · · · · · · · · · · · · · · · · · · · · · · · · · ·
· · · · · · · · · · · · · · · · · · · · · · · · · · ·

## GIVE THANKS
### what I'm grateful for today:

· · · · · · · · · · · · · · · · · · · · · · · · · · ·
· · · · · · · · · · · · · · · · · · · · · · · · · · ·
· · · · · · · · · · · · · · · · · · · · · · · · · · ·
· · · · · · · · · · · · · · · · · · · · · · · · · · ·
· · · · · · · · · · · · · · · · · · · · · · · · · · ·
· · · · · · · · · · · · · · · · · · · · · · · · · · ·
· · · · · · · · · · · · · · · · · · · · · · · · · · ·
· · · · · · · · · · · · · · · · · · · · · · · · · · ·

# REFLECTIONS & NOTES:

_____
_____
_____
_____
_____
_____
_____
_____
_____
_____
_____
_____
_____
_____
_____
_____

_____
_____
_____
_____
_____
_____
_____
_____
_____
_____
_____
_____
_____
_____
_____
_____

PRAY & WRITE TODAY'S VERSE:
Joshua 1:5

## STUDY NOTES: what does this scripture mean?

_____
_____
_____
_____
_____
_____
_____
_____
_____
_____

## DIG DEEPER: how does it apply to my life?

_____
_____
_____
_____
_____
_____
_____
_____
_____

TODAY'S date: _____

### PRAYER REQUESTS
for my family & children:

...............................................
...............................................
...............................................
...............................................
...............................................
...............................................
...............................................
...............................................

### GIVE THANKS
what I'm grateful for today:

...............................................
...............................................
...............................................
...............................................
...............................................
...............................................
...............................................
...............................................

# REFLECTIONS & NOTES:

PRAY & WRITE TODAY'S VERSE:
Exodus 14:14

## STUDY NOTES: what does this scripture mean?

_____
_____
_____
_____
_____
_____
_____
_____
_____
_____

## DIG DEEPER: how does it apply to my life?

_____
_____
_____
_____
_____
_____
_____
_____

TODAY'S date: _____

## PRAYER REQUESTS
### for my family & children:

. . . . . . . . . . . . . . . . . . . . . . . . . . . .
. . . . . . . . . . . . . . . . . . . . . . . . . . . .
. . . . . . . . . . . . . . . . . . . . . . . . . . . .
. . . . . . . . . . . . . . . . . . . . . . . . . . . .
. . . . . . . . . . . . . . . . . . . . . . . . . . . .
. . . . . . . . . . . . . . . . . . . . . . . . . . . .
. . . . . . . . . . . . . . . . . . . . . . . . . . . .
. . . . . . . . . . . . . . . . . . . . . . . . . . . .

## GIVE THANKS
### what I'm grateful for today:

. . . . . . . . . . . . . . . . . . . . . . . . . . . .
. . . . . . . . . . . . . . . . . . . . . . . . . . . .
. . . . . . . . . . . . . . . . . . . . . . . . . . . .
. . . . . . . . . . . . . . . . . . . . . . . . . . . .
. . . . . . . . . . . . . . . . . . . . . . . . . . . .
. . . . . . . . . . . . . . . . . . . . . . . . . . . .
. . . . . . . . . . . . . . . . . . . . . . . . . . . .
. . . . . . . . . . . . . . . . . . . . . . . . . . . .

# REFLECTIONS & NOTES:

PRAY & WRITE TODAY'S VERSE:
Jude 1:20-23

# STUDY NOTES: what does this scripture mean?

_____
_____
_____
_____
_____
_____
_____
_____
_____
_____

# DIG DEEPER: how does it apply to my life?

_____
_____
_____
_____
_____
_____
_____
_____
_____

TODAY'S date: _____

## PRAYER REQUESTS
### for my family & children:

..................................................
..................................................
..................................................
..................................................
..................................................
..................................................
..................................................
..................................................

## GIVE THANKS
### what I'm grateful for today:

..................................................
..................................................
..................................................
..................................................
..................................................
..................................................
..................................................
..................................................

# REFLECTIONS & NOTES:

PRAY & WRITE TODAY'S VERSE:
Galatians 5:22-26

**STUDY NOTES:** what does this scripture mean?

_____
_____
_____
_____
_____
_____
_____
_____
_____

**DIG DEEPER:** how does it apply to my life?

_____
_____
_____
_____
_____
_____
_____

**TODAY'S** date: _____

**PRAYER REQUESTS**
for my family & children:

.................................
.................................
.................................
.................................
.................................
.................................
.................................
.................................

**GIVE THANKS**
what I'm grateful for today:

.................................
.................................
.................................
.................................
.................................
.................................
.................................
.................................

# REFLECTIONS & NOTES:

PRAY & WRITE TODAY'S VERSE:
Galatians 5:14-15

# STUDY NOTES: *what does this scripture mean?*

_____
_____
_____
_____
_____
_____
_____
_____
_____

# DIG DEEPER: *how does it apply to my life?*

_____
_____
_____
_____
_____
_____
_____

## TODAY'S *date:* _____

### PRAYER REQUESTS
*for my family & children:*

. . . . . . . . . . . . . . . . . . . . . . . . . . . . . .
. . . . . . . . . . . . . . . . . . . . . . . . . . . . . .
. . . . . . . . . . . . . . . . . . . . . . . . . . . . . .
. . . . . . . . . . . . . . . . . . . . . . . . . . . . . .
. . . . . . . . . . . . . . . . . . . . . . . . . . . . . .
. . . . . . . . . . . . . . . . . . . . . . . . . . . . . .
. . . . . . . . . . . . . . . . . . . . . . . . . . . . . .
. . . . . . . . . . . . . . . . . . . . . . . . . . . . . .

### GIVE THANKS
*what I'm grateful for today:*

. . . . . . . . . . . . . . . . . . . . . . . . . . . . . .
. . . . . . . . . . . . . . . . . . . . . . . . . . . . . .
. . . . . . . . . . . . . . . . . . . . . . . . . . . . . .
. . . . . . . . . . . . . . . . . . . . . . . . . . . . . .
. . . . . . . . . . . . . . . . . . . . . . . . . . . . . .
. . . . . . . . . . . . . . . . . . . . . . . . . . . . . .
. . . . . . . . . . . . . . . . . . . . . . . . . . . . . .

# REFLECTIONS & NOTES:

PRAY & WRITE TODAY'S VERSE:
Philippians 4:12-13

# STUDY NOTES: what does this scripture mean?

_____
_____
_____
_____
_____
_____
_____
_____
_____
_____
_____

TODAY'S date: _____

## PRAYER REQUESTS
for my family & children:

. . . . . . . . . . . . . . . . . . . . . . . . . . .
. . . . . . . . . . . . . . . . . . . . . . . . . . .
. . . . . . . . . . . . . . . . . . . . . . . . . . .
. . . . . . . . . . . . . . . . . . . . . . . . . . .
. . . . . . . . . . . . . . . . . . . . . . . . . . .
. . . . . . . . . . . . . . . . . . . . . . . . . . .
. . . . . . . . . . . . . . . . . . . . . . . . . . .
. . . . . . . . . . . . . . . . . . . . . . . . . . .

# DIG DEEPER: how does it apply to my life?

_____
_____
_____
_____
_____
_____
_____
_____
_____

## GIVE THANKS
what I'm grateful for today:

. . . . . . . . . . . . . . . . . . . . . . . . . . .
. . . . . . . . . . . . . . . . . . . . . . . . . . .
. . . . . . . . . . . . . . . . . . . . . . . . . . .
. . . . . . . . . . . . . . . . . . . . . . . . . . .
. . . . . . . . . . . . . . . . . . . . . . . . . . .
. . . . . . . . . . . . . . . . . . . . . . . . . . .
. . . . . . . . . . . . . . . . . . . . . . . . . . .
. . . . . . . . . . . . . . . . . . . . . . . . . . .

# REFLECTIONS & NOTES:

PRAY & WRITE TODAY'S VERSE:
*Ruth 1:16-18*

# STUDY NOTES: what does this scripture mean?

_____
_____
_____
_____
_____
_____
_____
_____
_____
_____

# DIG DEEPER: how does it apply to my life?

_____
_____
_____
_____
_____
_____
_____
_____
_____

## TODAY'S date: _____

## PRAYER REQUESTS
_for my family & children:_

. . . . . . . . . . . . . . . . . . . . . . . . . .
. . . . . . . . . . . . . . . . . . . . . . . . . .
. . . . . . . . . . . . . . . . . . . . . . . . . .
. . . . . . . . . . . . . . . . . . . . . . . . . .
. . . . . . . . . . . . . . . . . . . . . . . . . .
. . . . . . . . . . . . . . . . . . . . . . . . . .
. . . . . . . . . . . . . . . . . . . . . . . . . .
. . . . . . . . . . . . . . . . . . . . . . . . . .

## GIVE THANKS
_what I'm grateful for today:_

. . . . . . . . . . . . . . . . . . . . . . . . . .
. . . . . . . . . . . . . . . . . . . . . . . . . .
. . . . . . . . . . . . . . . . . . . . . . . . . .
. . . . . . . . . . . . . . . . . . . . . . . . . .
. . . . . . . . . . . . . . . . . . . . . . . . . .
. . . . . . . . . . . . . . . . . . . . . . . . . .
. . . . . . . . . . . . . . . . . . . . . . . . . .
. . . . . . . . . . . . . . . . . . . . . . . . . .

# REFLECTIONS & NOTES:

PRAY & WRITE TODAY'S VERSE:
Ephesians 5:8—11

# STUDY NOTES: what does this scripture mean?

_____

_____

_____

_____

_____

_____

_____

_____

_____

_____

# DIG DEEPER: how does it apply to my life?

_____

_____

_____

_____

_____

_____

_____

_____

TODAY'S date: _____

## PRAYER REQUESTS
### for my family & children:

........................................

........................................

........................................

........................................

........................................

........................................

........................................

........................................

........................................

## GIVE THANKS
### what I'm grateful for today:

........................................

........................................

........................................

........................................

........................................

........................................

........................................

........................................

........................................

# REFLECTIONS & NOTES:

PRAY & WRITE TODAY'S VERSE:
*Proverbs* 31:25—31

# STUDY NOTES: what does this scripture mean?

_____

_____

_____

_____

_____

_____

_____

_____

_____

_____

## TODAY'S date: _____

### PRAYER REQUESTS
for my family & children:

...............................

...............................

...............................

...............................

...............................

...............................

...............................

...............................

...............................

# DIG DEEPER: how does it apply to my life?

_____

_____

_____

_____

_____

_____

_____

### GIVE THANKS
what I'm grateful for today:

...............................

...............................

...............................

...............................

...............................

...............................

...............................

...............................

# REFLECTIONS & NOTES:

PRAY & WRITE TODAY'S VERSE:
Psalm 127:3-5

**STUDY NOTES:** *what does this scripture mean?*

**TODAY'S** *date:* _____

_____

_____

_____

_____

_____

_____

_____

_____

_____

**PRAYER REQUESTS**
*for my family & children:*

...........................................

...........................................

...........................................

...........................................

...........................................

...........................................

...........................................

...........................................

**DIG DEEPER:** *how does it apply to my life?*

_____

_____

_____

_____

_____

_____

_____

_____

**GIVE THANKS**
*what I'm grateful for today:*

...........................................

...........................................

...........................................

...........................................

...........................................

...........................................

...........................................

103

# REFLECTIONS & NOTES:

PRAY & WRITE TODAY'S VERSE:
John 3:16-18

_____
_____
_____
_____
_____
_____
_____
_____
_____

## STUDY NOTES: *what does this scripture mean?*

_____
_____
_____
_____
_____
_____
_____
_____
_____
_____
_____

## DIG DEEPER: *how does it apply to my life?*

_____
_____
_____
_____
_____
_____
_____
_____

## TODAY'S *date:* _____

### PRAYER REQUESTS
*for my family & children:*

......................................
......................................
......................................
......................................
......................................
......................................
......................................
......................................

### GIVE THANKS
*what I'm grateful for today:*

......................................
......................................
......................................
......................................
......................................
......................................
......................................

# REFLECTIONS & NOTES:

Made in the USA
Middletown, DE
07 May 2021

39216306R00062